To H__ With Prohibition!

or

THE TRUTH ABOUT ALCOHOL FROM THE STANDPOINT OF A BIO-CHEMIST

∿

By

JAMES EMPRINGHAM, PH.D., D.SC., S.T.D.

∿

NATURAL LIFE SOCIETY
1609 W. NINTH STREET
LOS ANGELES, CALIF.

INTRODUCTORY NOTE
BY THE EDITORS

The following lecture is the notoriuo bomb-shell that Dr. Empringham exploded in a mass meeting of the united prohibition forces in 1925. This was the discourse that shocked the Temperance world.

Internationally known as an ardent advocate of Prohibition and author of several popular books on the subject, Dr. Empringham had been commissioned and financed by the Temperance Societies of England to make a nation-wide investigation of the prohibition situation in the United States.

Dr. Empringham firmly believed that such a survey would prove conclusively that prohibition was accomplishing much good and would eventually put a stop to intemperance, prevent crime, empty jails, and make it possible to rear young people without their knowing the taste of intoxicants.

But as this well-known "Dry" and his associates proceeded with their investigation in State after State, in an effort to learn actual conditions, they came to the conclusion that prohibitionists had made a mistake in attempting to force total abstinence on a country that was not prepared for it.

At the end of the survey, Dr. Empringham was invited to announce the result of his investigations at a mass meeting of the united temperance forces assembled at New York.

To the amazement and consternation of his audience, instead of eulogizing the 18th Amendment as a great step forward, he frankly stated that prohibition in America was doing much harm and was doomed to failure, because premature.

Dr. Empringham said: "The 18th Amendment will be abolished within a decade and will be succeeded by years of intemperance and lawlessness. But, eventually, prohibition will come back, and it will succeed, because it is the only logical solution of the liquor problem. This admirable state of affairs, however, cannot be brought about by coercion, but only as the result of many years of systematic, scientific education."

Every newspaper of almost every land carried the story of the Doctor's dramatic change of front. The bitterness against the Empringham report displayed by prohibitionists in Europe, was far more intense than in America, because the dry leaders of other lands were looking to the United States to prove that prohibition was the panacea for the world's ills. To these enthusiasts, Dr. Empringham's sudden change of front came as a great shock. He was denounced as a traitor and accused of having been bribed by the liquor traffic to bring in an adverse report. Many of the clergy in America, England, and other countries preached special sermons, in which they endeavored to minimize and ridicule the report, declaring that prohibition was not a failure as Empringham declared, but on the contrary it was an enormous success and that it was emptying jails and putting an end to crime.

After eight years, this discourse which sounded the first note of warning from a prominent "dry" that prohibition was not succeeding, and could not succeed because premature, seems quite conservative, and the program of education the Doctor recommended at that time would probably be endorsed by all prohibitionists today.   THE EDITORS.

4

To H__ With Prohibition!

CHAPTER I

THE TRUTH ABOUT ALCOHOL FROM THE STANDPOINT OF A BIO-CHEMIST

A lecture by Dr. Empringham delivered before the United Allies of Prohibition.
Town Hall, New York, January 21, 1926.

A philosopher of the fourth century compares the human brain to a menagerie and he likens our reason to the keeper or guard who must constantly watch and control the wild animals within the mind.

Modern psychology throws light upon this by teaching that the brain is composed of widely different areas. Just as an Atlantic liner is built up deck above deck, with the steerage and coal-holes below, and the finer cabins above, so our mind-centers vary in quality, and our actions are brutal or divine according as thought-power flows into the higher or lower of these chambers of the cerebrum.

Modern science explains this by saying our mentality is an inheritance from our prehistoric ancestors. In the countless ages of the past, our organs of thought were built up section by section. The small, original brain, merely controlled automatically such functions as blood-pumping, digestion and breathing. Then when creatures were given limbs, brain centers to move them were added. Later came areas for speech as the race learned vocal expression.

Finally, libraries of memory and laboratories of thought were added to the brain.

Now, in the growth and development of his own body, each man recapitulates this history of the race. He is an epitome of aeons of ancestors. In a few short years, nature builds man from a single cell, lower than a worm, up to the image of God.

A baby's brain merely controls circulation, breathing and muscular movement, as did the brains of the earliest animals, millions of years ago. Later, speech-centers are given the infant, then areas for higher thought.

The mentality of a child of twelve corresponds to that of our ancestors when they lived in forests. Hence, the delight of youngsters in climbing, building houses in trees and all sorts of rural sports. The games of children resemble the daily tasks of prehistoric man, because their minds are inherited and immature.

Modern life ties men to the shop, the office, to some form or other of exacting endeavor and the brain has developed centers which fit adults for such tasks; but all faculties acquired late in the history of the species are easily fatigued. We long for relaxation, to permit the psychic power to flow down to the older, well-worn channels of the brain. And this always happens when we imitate the primeval activities of the race. This is why camping, fishing, shooting give relaxation and rest.

Prehistoric man's chief business was hunting for food, swinging a club, throwing missiles and running in swift pursuit. Games like baseball rest and delight us because they employ the older, well-worn channels of the brain in repeating these racial activities—swinging a stick, throwing an object and running in hot pursuit.

According to modern philosophy, careful analysis shows that all sports and games of children and men are invariably an unconscious imitation of the daily activities of prehistoric man. The banker, attending a ball game, forgets he is a slave on Wall Street and yells like a savage of old.

Unfortunately, civilized man early found an artificial method of relieving his newer, overtaxed cerebrum centers and diverting the psychic power into the older parts of the brain. This consisted in paralyzing and sending to sleep the highest brain cells by means of narcotic poison. Just as the death-dealing gas of modern warfare blights and withers the last, tender shoots of the forest, leaving the older branches unharmed, so narcotics put out of commission the higher areas of the mind.

A great authority has calculated that more people are destroyed every year through addiction to narcotic, habit-forming drugs, than the wars of the world killed in a thousand years, from the days of Christ to the Battle of Waterloo. This sounds like an exaggeration, but I am inclined to think it may be true.

How many of you have thought of the millions of people that have been destroyed in India and throughout the Turkish Empire by slavery to the narcotic, habit-forming drug, hasheesh, or of the multitudes of natives of South America ruined through addiction to cocaine, or of the generations of Chinese wrecked by their abuse of opium and its derivatives—like morphine?

I remember when I was a youth in England, a professor of chemistry said in his lecture to our class: "Humanity's greatest curse is narcotic, habit-forming drugs. So-called civilized people pity barbarians for their addiction to narcotics, but we English are the worst drug fiends on the globe and we do not know it, because we think of ethyl-hydrate (alcohol) not as a drug but as a drink."

The people of Europe and America consume vast quantities of the liquid excretion which exudes from the bodies of certain microscopic organisms called mycoderma. Billions of these germs gather on the skins of grapes. When the grapes are crushed, these microscopic organisms fall into the juice, devour the sugar and excrete a narcotic, toxic poison which chemists call ethyl-hydrate, but the popular name for it is "alcohol."

When this refuse from the mycoderma is permitted to remain in the grape juice, we call the mixture "wine," when, by distillation, this liquid excreta has been separated from the wine, we name it "brandy."

We turn the starch of barley into a sugary solution, introduce some of the microscopic organisms, and when they have all committed suicide in their own toxic excretion, we label the result "beer." We extract this excretion, this habit-forming drug, from the beer and then call it "whiskey."

There is a poplar delusion that alcohol (the excreta of the bacteria we have been describing) is a beverage. We talk of the curse of "drink," but alcohol is no more a drink than is morphine or cocaine. We imagine alcohol to be a beverage, because whenever we see this drug, it is always mixed with a large quantity of water. Beer is generally ninety-five per cent water—wine about eighty-nine per cent water, and whiskey fifty per cent water.

Of course it is the water mixed with the alcohol which makes people think of this diluted poison as a drink or beverage.

If a chemist extracted every drop of water from a barrel of beer, and a man drank one glass of the beer from which all the water had been removed, he would die in an hour or so. The waterless beer would not quench his thirst, but would kill him by robbing his tissues of moisture. A man has drunk a pint of chloroform and recovered, but no man ever drank a pint of pure alcohol—that is, alcohol without any water—and ever lived to tell the tale.

Prohibitionists make the mistake of continually talking about the curse of "drink." Alcohol is not a drink, but a poisonous, habit-forming drug. If alcohol were a drink, then any prohibitory legislation would be a sumptuary law, and all history proves that sumptuary laws, (enactments regulating what people must eat, drink and wear) are worse than useless and cannot be enforced.

Just so long as dry advocates keep calling alcohol "drink," they will never have effective prohibition. If alcohol were a beverage it would be foolish to attempt to force men not to drink it.

Alcohol was formerly considered a stimulant. It is now known to be a depressant. Yet, in a way, it stimulates because it depresses. When Fifth Avenue, New York, is closed, traffic on the lower parallel avenues is greatly increased. So the lower psychic channels of the brain are stimulated when the higher pathways are closed by narcotics. The last, fairest

9

flower of the civilized mind is modesty, and modesty is the first to fade under the fumes of alcohol. For this reason, intoxicants act as lubricants, oiling the wheels of social intercourse.

The silent, shy and retiring, grow eloquent with the first glass of wine, and then more talkative still, as caution, discretion and judgment are softly soothed into slumber. In such happy moments, a man tells how his grandfather was hanged for horse stealing. A little more wine and the happy man grows quarrelsome. That part of his brain which directed his forefathers of the jungle, now awakens as the civilized man falls asleep. And now he becomes dangerous. For the criminal life of today was the normal life of the cave-man.

A little more wine and the centers of speech are affected. Then those of muscular activities. He stutters and stumbles. Let him pour enough alcohol and he may put to sleep the deep buried centers that control heart and diaphragm, and the man never wakens again.

To the popular mind a man is not intoxicated until it shows in his talk and his walk, but innumerable scientific tests prove that no person can take one glass of beer without paralyzing, to a measurable degree, the highest centers of the brain. The man's closest friends may not detect it, but science has invented delicate, psychometric instruments for measuring the effect of such drugs. Just as the telescope makes known many stars the unaided eye cannot see—as the microscope shows everywhere bacteria, microbes and germs—as the radio-receiver digs sounds out of the silent air—so the instruments of modern science reveal drunken brain tracks in apparently-sober men.

Beer and wine are attractive for no other reason except that they intoxicate—that is, the alcohol they contain puts to sleep the finer cerebrum cells. It also affects nerve reaction. Many experiments prove that in such tasks as typesetting, shooting, or driving a car, one glass of beer will lower efficiency nearly twenty per cent. That is why some accidents happen. If beer did not intoxicate—if it did not produce that feeling of euphoria which results from the relaxation caused by the partial paralysis of the higher brain—no one would want it.

Now, rest for the overtaxed nerves is doubtless extremely desirable. Alcohol gives such relaxation. Is not, therefore, a moderate use of this drug a most desirable habit? Multitudes think so. It might be objected that the statistics of all life insurance companies prove that such moderate use of this narcotic shortens life by ten or twelve years. Many would say: "What of it?" For a key which opens a paradise where boredom and grief are forgotten, many would give years of life; but the indictment brought by science and society against alcohol is much more serious than the charge that it shortens the life of the user—more serious, also, than the fact that the later depression outweighs the earlier joy, as surely as the morning-after follows the night-before.

The charge against alcohol is that it puts to sleep the keeper of our mental menagerie. A trainer of wild animals in a circus once said that if he permitted his mind to be diverted for a moment, the brutes would tear him to pieces. Alcohol puts to sleep the keeper of our mental menagerie and turns loose on society the bear and the cave-man that slumber in every brain.

In all our pastimes and sports, the higher mind-tracts are rested but never put out of commission. Alcohol sandbags the civilized brain and rouses the unguarded savage. For this reason, Gladstone said: "Alcohol has in it the combined evils of war, pestilence and famine." Not because it here and there makes a man so drunk it shows in his talk and his walk, but because it daily robs multitudes of sober, respectable people of modesty, discretion and judgment, rendering them liable to physical, mental and moral accidents, and meanwhile giving no clue that these seemingly sober people are drunk in their higher brain areas.

Because it puts to sleep modesty, alcohol recruits the cesspools of commercialized vice with a ceaseless flood of white slaves. Because it handicaps judgment, alcohol sweeps so-called sober young men to those lurid swamps of disease—I mean the red-light districts—that men, free from all alcohol, shun.

Our first line of defense against the attacks of disease are the white blood corpuscles which constantly guard our lives by devouring the dangerous microbes. But the microscope shows one or two glasses of beer will so paralyze these little soldiers in our bodies that they cannot protect us from the onslaught of disease germs.

Alcohol is one of the few poisons that adversely affects the germ-plasm, thus injuring pre-natal life. Ethyl hydrate is, therefore, a racial poison.

Six years ago, when prohibition was written into the Constitution of the United States, many enthusiasts believed that the millenium would come at once.

Personally, I believed and hoped that the liquor problem in America had been settled for all time, and that the custom of using this dangerous narcotic as a beverage would gradually come to an end, as the confirmed victims of the habit died out, and no recruits were made to take the place of the old slaves of the drug.

But as we prosecuted our investigation into the workings of the 18th Amendment, in every State of the Union, the sad fact that prohibition was aggravating and increasing the evils it was intended to cure, gradually forced itself upon the minds of my associates and myself. We perceived also that it was creating a general disregard for law, and other evils that were worse than alcoholic intemperance.

Before we had the 18th Amendment, if a youth attended a dance with a whiskey flask in his hip-pocket, he would have been shunned and ostracized, but today the boy who goes to a party equipped in this way is greeted as a hero. In pre-prohibition days, an intoxicated young girl had never been seen —today they disgrace every gathering where young people meet for a good time.

Prohibition is breeding a generation that has no respect for authority or legal enactments.

A great philosopher once said, "Laws are not made—they are discovered."

Before a law is written on the statute books, it must be first engraved on the hearts of the people. Every man must instinctively recognize it as a wise and just law or it will arouse resentment and disobedience.

It is true that the laws against stealing, murder, and adultery are frequently disobeyed, but every person has an innate, instinctive appreciation of the fact that these regulations of society are right and just.

The legislative enactments which seek to render the operation of automobiles safe for the community are frequently broken, even by nice, respectable citizens, but these violators of traffic regulations know in their hearts that the ordinances they are breaking are necessary and good.

The trouble begins when legislators make laws that are an unwarranted, needless restriction of the rights and liberties of the individual. Then resentment, and a desire to break the law that is thought to be unjust, is at once born in the mind of every person who believes the enactment an unnecessary, impertinent interference with his personal liberty.

To millions of people, the 18th Amendment is just that kind of unreasonable and unjust law, for they think that alcohol is a beverage. People have not been educated to understand that this drug is really a narcotic, habit-forming poison that puts to sleep a man's higher brain-centers, even when imbibed in the smallest quantities, and thus renders the drugged individual dangerous to the community, because his lower faculties are still awake, while the higher brain-centers are sleeping.

Alcohol is also a protoplasmic poison and does more or less harm to the persons who drink it. But that is not the chief reason why it should be prohibited by law.

Sugar, coffee, and tobacco are also injurious but the harm resulting from the consumption of these things is confined to the person who takes them. A murderer never tries to kill his victim with cigars or sugar—that method would be too slow.

But the injury done by alcohol is not confined to the person who takes this poisonous drug. When a man climbs into his car with a cigar in his mouth, he is no more of a menace to his fellow men than if he were not smoking; but when he sits in the driver's seat after consuming even one or two glasses of beer he is dangerous to other people, because even the slight amount of alcohol he has consumed has, to some extent, put out of commission his higher brain-centers of reason, discretion, caution, and good judgment though he might be pronounced sober by all ordinary tests. Therefore, the manufacture and sale of alcohol should be prohibited; but in order to make such legislation effective it will first be necessary to have many years of intensive education to make all people understand that alcohol is not a drink, not a beverage, but a narcotic, habit-forming drug, dangerous to society because it paralyzes the latest evolved part of the brain—the section that enables us to live in civilized society—and diverts the psychic power into the lower channels that served our savage ancestors.

Alcohol is really more dangerous to the community than morphine, yet people generally do not resent the laws that restrict the sale of opium and its derivatives.

I have known many so-called morphine fiends, but these poor slaves are always very much ashamed of their weakness. I never knew a morphine fiend to go up to some friend on the street corner and slap him on the back and say, "Come around to the drug store, old man, and have a morphine on me."

In England the favorite narcotic is chloral hydrate, but no man invites his friends to come around to the drug store and join him in a chloral hydrate. He is ashamed of his habit. Why, then, should a man, with such joyous pride, invite his friend to take ethyl hydrate—that is, alcohol. It is because he is in total ignorance of the fact that ethyl hydrate, like chloral hydrate, belongs to the same family of narcotic, habit-forming drugs.

The trouble with prohibition is that it came too soon. It arrived before the people understood it and before they were ready for it.

When our sons were in France fighting for their lives, we started the slogan: "Whiskey is wasting grain; bread will win the war. Let us prohibit the sale of alcohol to save our boys at the front."

And at that time of excitement every person was willing to make any sacrifice that would help to put an end to the conflict.

In other words, Prohibition was Uncle Sam's war-bride. He married in haste, and he will repent at leisure.

Mark my words. In spite of all that is being said about the 18th Amendment emptying jails and putting an end to crime and intemperance, I prophesy that within ten years* the mounting tide of indignation at what so many regard as an unjust interference with their personal liberty, will sweep the 18th Amendment into oblivion, and then whiskey will come back like a flood, and the condition of the Nation will be much worse than it was before the days of prohibition. (Shouts of "No! No! Absurd! Traitor! Make him sit down!")

*FOOTNOTE: This lecture was given in January, 1926.

I believe prohibition will fail because I now know the people were not ready for it, and I predict the temperance situation, or rather the intemperance situation, will be worse after prohibition has passed, than it was before the 18th Amendment was enacted, because we will then have a new generation that has not been educated to the fact that alcohol is in reality not a drink, not a beverage, but a dangerous, narcotic, habit-forming drug.

Unfortunately, the moment the 18th Amendment became a fact, the temperance societies stopped their educational campaign, and the public schools thought there was no longer any need to waste time teaching the youth of the nation the dangers of whiskey, beer, and wine, because in theory alcohol had ceased to exist.

However, the necessity for sound scientific instruction on this point is greater today than ever. It should be begun at once. It should be carried out with a thoroughness a thousand times greater than ever before and must continue many, many years, and in due time there will be no more difficulty in legislating successfully against ethyl hydrate than against chloral hydrate, because all men will understand that alcohol is not a drink—not a beverage— but a dangerous, narcotic, habit-forming drug, and a menace to the safety of mankind. And when that day comes, the world will be happier.

CHAPTER II

IF JESUS DRANK WINE, CAN WE BE HIS FOLLOWERS UNLESS WE DO LIKEWISE?

At the marriage of Cana, our Lord made wine.

Learned authorities in all ages have given reasons for believing this wine did not contain alcohol. These scholars have said that the Jews in Biblical times understood the art of preventing fermentation and they insist that the eleven different Hebrew words that are all uniformly rendered "wine" in our English translation, are used with precision by the original writers to discriminate between fermented and unfermented grape juice. Dr. E. L. Eaton in his book, "Winning the Fight Against Drink," ably presents this theory of unfermented wine.

Presbyterians, Baptists, Methodists and other non-Episcopal bodies, assume our Lord did not employ intoxicants.

On the other hand, Episcopalians—Eastern, Roman and Anglican—have generally favored the theory that the wine employed by our Lord on various occasions was fermented, and therefore, contained alcohol. Alcohol is simply the excretion of a microscopic organism that always abounds in the atmosphere except in the arctic regions.

The case for those who insist they can prove that Jesus used fermented wine on one occasion, at least —the institution of the Last Supper—is strongly presented by Dr. Tyson, of Princeton, in a recent letter to "The Churchman." This well-known scholar says:

"Belief that 'fermented wine was used at the institution of the Lord's Supper,' is based historically upon the fact that the existence of unfermented grape juice in Palestine would have been an impossibility during the Passover season. On the other hand, the juice of the previous season's grapes had long since become either vinegar, inasmuch as the Jews possessed no knowledge of an antisepsis necessary to check fermentation, or, if 'bottled,' a true fermented wine. On the other hand, there could be no fresh grape juice from the crop of the current season, for the reason that the latest possible date of the Passover is approximately two months earlier than the earliest possible period of the ripening of the grapes."

Now let us assume that the above reasoning is unanswerable, and that our Lord did use juice polluted with the excretions of mycoderma because the science of that day had not discovered a way of protecting the juice of the grape from the ravages of these microscopic vermin.

The undeveloped condition of society two thousand years ago thrust many inconveniences upon our Blessed Lord which we are no longer called upon to endure. The Divine Master and His disciples, with bleeding feet, tramped many a weary mile over the uneven, stony roads of Palestine, but Christians now need not follow His steps in this respect, for we have smooth highways and cars with cushioned wheels. In His journeys, Jesus drank the warm, disgusting water from the odorous skin-bottles. Palestine Christians may now refresh themselves from a cool, clean, "thermos," without casting any reflections on the habits of their Master. The water of those days was often dangerous as well as unpleasant. The congested, filthy cities of that age had no health department facilities for analyzing the water, but modern Christians need not quench their thirst from germ-infected pools and cisterns because the Son of Man suffered such hardships.

Jesus ate the tasteless, dried fruits of the East because the art of canning was unknown. Today, Christians may enjoy scientifically preserved fruits and still be His loyal followers.

In Christ's day, surgeons used the knife while their patients writhed in conscious agony. Often the sympathetic ears of Jesus must have been pierced with the shrieks of suffering that today would be soothed with anaesthetics. What multitudes died from the slow torture of infected wounds because germs and germicides were alike undreamed of!

Since Jesus was born in Bethlehem, innumerable scientific discoveries have completely transformed man's method of living.

During the last twenty-five years, without blare of trumpets, a truth has been brought to light that will have a greater effect upon the world's history than any other event of the last two thousand years. I refer to the epoch-making discovery of the nature and physiological effect of alcohol.

Ardent Spirits, or to use the scientific name, ethyl hydrate, we now know is a protoplasmic poison—the foe of efficiency and health. Two thousand years ago, men regarded the fermented juices of fruits as the aqua vitae,—the water of life. Many may ask: "How came men of the Old World to regard alcohol as the source of longevity when, as a matter of fact, this drug is humanity's greatest foe?" Alcohol has not always been man's worst enemy. In our Lord's day, wine was justly esteemed the elixir of life. Frequently it was almost essential to human existence.

Tea rendered the same service to China that alcohol did to Greece, Rome and the Holy Land, and in much the same way. Therefore, the Chinese attribute to tea lifegiving qualities which that pleasant, comparatively harmless beverage does not possess. How did tea acquire its reputation for warding off disease and prolonging life among the Chinese? In this way. In ancient times, the Chinese were a very filthy people. The population was fearfully congested. There was no municipal system for removing sewerage or supplying water. The garbage and waste products of the home were flung into the narrow streets to decay, with the result that epidemics of typhoid and similar germ-diseases swept at frequent intervals through the land. It came to be observed, in ancient China, that families which drank a decoction obtained from boiling the leaves of the tea-shrubs did not die from typhoid and similar epidemics. Magical, life-giving virtues were, in consequence, ascribed to tea. No one then suspected that the beneficial effects were simply the result of the germ-destroying action of the boiled water without which the beverage could not be brewed.

In a very similar way, in the early, barbarous, unsanitary condition of society, alcohol obtained credit as a life preserver which was not merited by any virtues the drug itself possessed.

Picture the condition of an American city with a large population, if there were no sewerage system, no sense of responsibility on the part of the municipal authorities to remove garbage and other products of the population, and no water supply except

21

wells and cisterns. Then consider how much more dreadful the condition must have been with the narrow streets and hot climate of eastern lands like Palestine. Tourists who have seen (and smelt) old Cairo, especially as it was a few years ago, when the garbage was left to decay in the streets, and the Cairo authorities felt their duty ended with sending the perfume-man twice a day to sprinkle the streets with scented water from a huge skin bottle, can form a picture of what most oriental cities must have been two thousand years ago. No wonder frequent epidemics scourged the land.

Wine then was regarded as the most health-giving drink, the nectar of heaven, the gift of the gods, that kept men from dying. And not without reason. Those who drank nothing but grape juice, fermented or otherwise, did not die of typhoid—not because there was any virtue in the wine, but because those who imbibed the "fruit of the vine" avoided the disease-impregnated water. The vine drank of the dew and the rain and preserved in skins, offered mankind a beverage free from contamination. But you will say, "Was not the alcohol of the wine just as much a protoplasmic poison three thousand years ago as it is today?" Undoubtedly, but it was not so deadly as the polluted water of those filthy cities. Of the two evils, the poison in the wine was incomparably less than the poison in the water of those pools and cisterns.

Some years ago, with a small party of students of the British Institute of Archaeology, I was staying in the dirty little native village which now marks the site of the Temple of Diana in ancient Ephesus. Typhoid broke out and the very same advice St.

Paul gave Timothy when that young minister of Christ was sojourning in that same city was given to us by the natives: "Drink no water, drink wine," and though most of our party were total abstainers on principle, we saved our lives by most religiously following the apostolical advice.

When St. Paul was in Laodicea, he wrote to Timothy in Ephesus: "Drink no longer water, drink wine." Did the Apostle understand the reason why wine was better than the water of Ephesus? Undoubtedly he did not. St. Paul knew nothing of the germ nature of disease. Microscopes had not been invented. The Apostle doubtless shared the popular erroneous opinion of his day that wine had wonderful life-giving qualities. If St. Paul had known that boiled water would have had all the virtues and none of the disadvantages of wine, he would have commended the kettle rather than the wine-skin. If St. Paul had known that anaesthetics would have prevented the fearful agony of surgical operations, or, if he had known that blood-poisoning was the result of microbes and that wounds could be made to heal by the application of germicides, he would have so advised his generation and the world would have been saved from untold suffering. St. Paul gave the best advice possible in his day when he warned Timothy about the water and recommended wine. If, instead of giving this commendable advice, St. Paul had urged Timothy to start a propaganda for prohibition, he would have been two thousand years ahead of his day and would have done more harm than good.

When Christ made wine, he did a patriotic and righteous act and stamped with His approval a cus-

23

tom essential to the well-being of the pestilence-cursed cities of those days.

Were Christ upon earth today, would he still give His friends wine? I think he would not. There would be no reason for his so doing. Many things Jesus did when He was on earth He would not do today. As an obedient child, Christ in the Nazareth home often went to the common flame to procure a light for the domestic hearth. Today He would secure the same result by a less laborious process. Many actions proper in Christ's day have been rendered foolish or wrong by the changed conditions of society.

Herbert Spencer, in his "Synthetic Philosophy," says: "Customs relatively right in a lower age become wrong when detrimental to conditions more advanced." Spencer points out that slavery was once right. There was a time when a law prohibiting slavery would have been immoral. The victors in warfare in the early history of the world tortured their captives, then slew and ate them. The conqueror who first set the example of consigning his captives to work in his stables or garden instead of having them butchered and broiled for a banquet, made a great moral advance. Slavery is better than cannibalism.

Think what a self-sacrificing, noble deed the act of making the first slaves may have been. Picture the leader of some fierce tribe in the hour of victory. He is famished with hunger. He has from childhood been accustomed to consider human flesh the choicest kind of food. The killing and eating of captives has been for ages the religious custom of his tribe. The ravenous appetite of this victorious battle leader

24

craves satisfaction. But ere he butchers the captives reserved for his table, a nobler thought dawns on the savage chieftain. He pities his fallen foes and decides to save their lives to make them the servants of his tribe. Thus slavery was born and the father of that institution by restraining his cannibalistic instincts to do a generous deed, was a man after God's own heart. Slavery was at one time the world's highest morality. Many customs immoral today were virtuous and commendable in an early stage of the evolution of humanity.

Shallow men have scoffed at the Old Testament for what they have denounced as its low morality. They have said: "If God be the same yesterday, today, and forever, why are certain institutions approved in the Old Testament and condemned in the New?" These critics forget that human circumstances change, though God does not. Humanity has slowly progressed from savagery to the present stage of semi-civilization.

Polygamy, prohibited today, was a virtue at an earlier stage of history. The existence of tribes in constant conflict with hostile hordes depended upon rapid increase in numbers. Therefore, to the moralists of early days polygamy seemed a great virtue necessary for a tribe's existence. Critics who express astonishment that Jehovah encouraged Abraham and other patriarchs in their polygamy should remember that conditions have changed and that "customs relatively right in a lower age become wrong when detrimental to conditions more advanced."

Two thousand years ago for a surgeon to amputate a limb without an anaesthetic was quite proper. To do the same thing today would be immoral and illegal. The law prohibits such operations. But a law prohibiting a surgeon from using the knife without anaesthetics would have been foolish and immoral in Christ's day for then such gifts of God as anaesthetics were unknown.

In Old Testament times, Jehovah prohibited swine's flesh as food. What the conditions then were that made such prohibition expedient we do not know. Our Lord was a Jew and it is quite certain that by His example He gave His sanction to this prohibition of pork. If in all matters we in this day are to be bound by our Lord's example, what about eating swine's flesh? Do those who insist upon the sanctity of imbibing the drug, alcohol, on the basis of Christ's alleged example, abstain from the use of pork? We are inquiring in the interests of consistency. It will make some difference in the weight we attach to their utterances if we discover that they only take our Lord's example when it seems to favor their weakness for the narcotic drug, alcohol.

Jesus never married. Are the pleaders for the abolition of the 18th Amendment following Christ's example in this particular?

There were no women at the Last Supper. Do the clergymen who appeal to the alleged example of Christ for the beverage use of wine, administer the Holy Eucharist in this respect after the example of our Lord?

Let us be consistent. To do exactly the things Christ did is not, by that fact, to follow His example. To have the Spirit of Christ and to do now what He would have us do, is to follow Him. The man who simply attempts to reproduce identical actions is an ape and not a follower,—just as a man who simply repeats the Master's words is a parrot and not a prophet. If any man has not the Spirit of Christ, he is none of His, and God pity the man, clergyman or layman, who can harmonize his idea of the Spirit of Christ with the modern liquor traffic —either the "legitimate" business as under license, or, what is worse, the distribution of alcoholic poisons by underworld thieves and murderers—as now obtains.

In Christ's day, when whiskey and other liquors were unknown because the art of distillation had not been discovered and when wine was the only safe drink because the water was filled with disease germs, of which the science of those days did not dream, Christ did not condemn fermented grape juice for the very good reason that wine in those days was the only safe drink. But conditions have changed. The microscope has revealed the danger of polluted water, and we more truly follow the Master today when we teach the truth about alcohol than by giving our approval and moral support to a traffic which has in it the combined evils of "war, pestilence, and famine."

THE NATURAL LIFE SOCIETY

The Natural Life Society might be called an organization for combatting the habitual use of poisons.

It is now known that practically all maladies—all forms of sickness, old age, and death—are caused by toxins or poisons.

Nothing should enter the body but natural foods and pure water.

Such poisons as alcohol and tobacco throw an additional and unnecessary burden upon the already overworked anti-toxic organs of the body.

Our campaign of education is directed not only against alcohol, but against tobacco, opium, morphine, cocaine, heroine, and even coffee, tea, condiments, and all other poisonous substances which tend to undermine health and to shorten life. Too often the body itself is a poison factory.

Time does not bring about the senile condition we call old age. This is the result of toxins which enter the blood stream or are generated within the body.

The following chapters taken from Doctor Empringham's book, *"Youth Regained by Intestinal Gardening,"* will show something of the scope of our work.

The Natural Life Society exists for the purpose of waging a fight against all poisons which shorten life. Our method is to disseminate reliable, scientific information by means of lectures and literature.

The members of our lecture staff are glad at any time to address gatherings of all kinds, large or small, without remuneration. Our workers are volunteers and there are no fees. We make no charge for admission and do not insist upon any offering.

Our General Secretary, Doctor Empringham, is now in Los Angeles and can be secured for a limited number of talks.

Address:

NATURAL LIFE SOCIETY
1609 WEST NINTH STREET
LOS ANGELES, CALIFORNIA
TELEPHONE: FEderal 7320

Chapter III

IS MAN'S BODY POTENTIALLY IMMORTAL?

Time Does Not Make Us Senile.
The Body is Continually Renewed.
Toxins from Cell-Refuse, and Bowel-Bacteria, Bring Sickness, Old Age, and Death.

Alcohol, an excretion of fermentative germs, is a mortal poison when concentrated. That is the reason it is impossible to obtain more than thirteen per-cent of alcohol except by distillation.

On one occasion a gentleman from the underworld confided to me that he was ready to give a large sum of money to anyone who would show

---

The following chapters are from
YOUTH REGAINED BY INTESTINAL GARDENING
By
Dr. Empringham
Bound in Cloth and Gold
35 Chapters; 250 pages; One Dollar
NATURAL LIFE SOCIETY
1609 W. Ninth Street
Los Angeles, Calif.

---

him how to make alcohol "without boiling the stuff."

He explained that his method of making spirits was first of all to turn grape-juice into wine by the natural process of fermentation. He then boiled the wine, collected and cooled the alcoholic vapor by means of a still, and, by thus separating the alcohol from the water, he produced whiskey from beer and brandy from wine.

But he said this method was open to the objection that it disturbed the neighbors, by disseminating a strong odor, with the result that more than once he had been compelled, temporarily, to discontinue his important work.

He was therefore anxious to know how to make alcohol so strong by fermentation, that it would not be necessary to boil the product to obtain whiskey or brandy.

I told my mysterious visitor, that chemistry could do nothing to enable him to carry out his ambition.

I said, "Alcohol is simply the excretion of microscopic germs." It might be called the urine of bacteria. Fermentative microbes are always present on the skins of grapes. When the fruit is pressed they get into the juice, eat up the sugar and excrete the liquid we call alcohol.

The waste products of all living creatures are poisonous. The refuse from these little wine-makers is no exception. When these microbes have polluted the juice with thirteen per-cent of alcohol they are all killed by their own toxic excretion. This is the reason it is impossible to produce beer or wine with more spirit than thirteen per-cent.

ALL ANIMALS COMMIT SUICIDE — But the germs that make wine and beer are not the only creatures that commit suicide by re-absorbing their own waste products. All animals, including man, eventually destroy themselves in exactly the same way. Were it not for this tragic fact, man, and all other animals, would be potentially immortal.

The microscope proves that the body of every living being is simply an assemblage of tiny cells. Each one of these cells is a complete creature that breathes, eats, drinks and excretes its wastes of digestion, and at the end of a few weeks dies, and is carried away by the blood stream, sepulchered for a short time in the lower bowel, and eventually cast out from the body with the feces.

But each of these microscopic living bricks, of which our flesh is composed, gives birth to a successor before it expires. Therefore our bodies are in a continual flux. Little by little, every day we die, and just as gradually and as continuously, every moment, section by section we are being reborn. The oldest man therefore is but a baby. Scarcely a particle of his body is more than a year old. Even our bones, through the medium of the microscopic blood-tubes by which they are intersected, pass away piece by piece and are constantly renewed.

Rome is called the "Eternal City." It has flourished for thousands of years and is as young as ever, because new citizens are born every hour to replace those that die. In consequence of this continuous regeneration there is no reason why the metropolis of Italy, or any city, should not survive so long as our planet exists.

In the same way the bodies of all animals are composed of innumerable cells that are renewed at frequent intervals. Why then are not all animals as eternal as Rome? What is the cause of those senile. degenerative changes we falsely attribute to "age?" What is the cause of that phenomena we call natural death? This is one of the profoundest problems that confronts modern biology.

The answer seems to be that our body-cells are perpetually poisoned, and often killed, by their own toxic excretions, before such sick cells succeed in generating a successor. We die daily, piecemeal, little by little.

If it were possible to count our body-cells — that is, to take a census of the little living bricks of which our flesh is composed — at twenty-one years of age, it might be found that a man has a population of a hundred billion cells. But every year the number grows less, because the tiny units are continually being poisoned and pass away, leaving behind no successors.

Our bodies, in course of time, become honeycombed with innumerable microscopic cavities, from which dead cells have dropped out, and after reaching maturity, we should begin to dwindle in size and weight, were it not for the fact that the microscopic holes from which the dead cells have fallen, are promptly filled up with foreign matter, mostly in the form of lime and other inorganic salts. It is for this reason that old animals used as food are tougher and less nutritious than young ones. Sometimes the cavities left by departed body-cells are refilled with fat. This results in what is known as fatty degeneration of the heart and of other organs.

TIME CANNOT MAKE US OLD — One of the results of this replacing of lost cells by dead matter is what is known as arterio-sclerosis or hardening of the arteries. Our blood-tubes lose their elasticity as the living bricks of which our tissues are built are replaced by inorganic mineral salts, fat or other dead material. As a result, the lumen, or passage through the blood-tubes, decreases in size, requiring more effort on the part of the heart to maintain the circulation and in consequence the blood pressure rises. These are spoken of as symptoms of increasing age. But in reality the years we have lived have nothing to do with these degenerative changes. They are entirely due to the poisonous waste-matter that our cells are continually dumping into the blood-stream.

Time has not the slightest effect upon our bodies. It does not wrinkle the brow, whiten the hair, or produce those senile characteristics which we falsely attribute to age.

GLANDS DESTROY POISONS — Nature does her best to protect all of her creatures against the poisonous excreta of the cells. She accomplishes this in two ways. First by the blood-stream, which acts as a sewer to carry away this refuse eliminated by the tissues. Insects and other invertebrate creatures that are not furnished with a drainage system, such as the veins provide, are always short-lived.

Secondly, the higher animals are equipped with glands for the purpose of destroying the poisonous wastes. These antitoxic organs are always in a rudimentary form at birth and are gradually perfected during the growth period.

For this reason it is not wise to permit young people to indulge in tobacco, alcohol, coffee and other poisons which older persons, with fully matured glands, often enjoy without being conscious of injury.

WHY ANIMALS LIVE SEVEN TIMES THEIR GROWTH-PERIOD — Nature requires time to perfect her poison-destroying gland-system, and this fact accounts for the well known law, that the life-duration of any creature is seven times the length of its growth period. In a normal environment, any animal that takes two years to reach maturity, may expect to live fourteen. Horses that continue to grow for three years live till they are twenty-one. Elephants require forty years to reach the adult stage and it is said survive over two hundred years. Some insects are fully grown in twenty-four hours and never live more than one week.

Human beings attain their majority at about twenty-one, though they often continue to grow physically, for twelve months longer. Therefore, by the analogy of all other creatures, men and women might naturally expect to live seven times their growth period, or about one hundred and fifty years. But statistics prove that the average length of human life is about forty years — not even twice the length of time that elapses from birth to the termination of adolescence.

CHAPTER IV
WHY WE GROW OLD

Why is mankind comparatively much shorter lived than the lower animals? Why do not we, like other creatures, survive seven times the length of our growth period? The answer seems to be that we are continually poisoning ourselves in various ways.

Animals, as we have seen, are injured and eventually killed by the toxic wastes of their tissue-cells. But, human beings have an additional and still more dangerous source of infection. This is due to the fact that the colon or lower bowel of the average person is a sewer or cesspool, at all times polluted with billions of poisonous microbes that are continually generating virulent toxins.

No one would want to live in a house if the cellar were swarming with dangerous vermin, yet most people seem content to harbor within their bodies, in the lower bowel, tiny micro-organisms that are pouring out poisons every moment.

Many will say, "How can these dangerous germs get into the body?" In reply we would state that every mouthful of food that we eat is invariably swarming with microbes. These bacteria play a useful — in fact, an absolutely indispensible part in the drama of life on this planet by redistributing the elements of which all living things are composed.

This disintegration of organized matter by Nature's energetic little wreckers, the bacteria, we call putrefaction or decay. Unfortunately this good work of the protein-splitting microbes is always accompanied by the production of deadly toxins. Bacteria begin their work of tearing down tissues the moment any creature ceases to live.

BAD BACTERIA CANNOT STAND ACID— These putrefactive microbes are hard to destroy. They may be frozen in ice for years without injury, and in the spore-form, often survive boiling and baking. But these hardy poison-producing germs have one vulnerable point. They are at once paralyzed and put out of commission by any kind of acid, however mild.

Nature well knows this weak point of the bad bacteria and she continually makes use of this weapon to defend living creatures against poisons from this source.

Every mouthful of food we eat is swarming with invisible germs that would generate toxins in our intestines if they had their own way. But the moment these dangerous little bacteria slip down the throat into the stomach, Nature gives them a bath of hydrochloric acid in the gastric juice. This acid kills many germs, but it merely paralyzes or puts to sleep, the more resistant varieties, by compelling them to assume what is known as the spore-form.

Nature assumes that the food will be digested and the refuse, with the sleeping bacteria, will be expelled from the body long before this incubation period of twenty-four hours has expired.

Food is seldom more than three, or at most, four hours in the stomach, and a similar length of time in the small intestine; and during this period the nourishment is digested and absorbed into the blood-stream, and the refuse is discharged into the colon. If the bowels were emptied promptly after each meal, the putrefactive bacteria would be expelled from the body while still paralyzed from the effects of the acid stomach-juices.

But civilized life has brought about a universal condition of constipation, because the conventions of society do not permit of an evacuation of the bowels whenever and wherever the impulse is felt. This delay so retards the "motility period," that many people retain the food-residues for forty-eight hours or more, in spite of the fact that their bowels may move once or even twice every day.

WHY CONSTIPATION DOES HARM — As a result of this tardiness the putrefactive bacteria, that were put to sleep by the acid of the gastric juice in the stomach, wake up in the lower bowel and begin to generate. Each germ, as we have said, divides and becomes two, every twenty minutes.

At this rate, each microbe becomes the ancestor of over eight millions, in the course of twenty-four hours, as any person who takes the trouble to figure it out will discover. These germs cause the food residues to putrefy and thus produce deadly poisons.

One might naturally say: "Well, if the colon of the average person is continually filled with dangerous poisons produced by bad bacteria, why are not such people killed at once by their own toxins?"

The answer is, that Nature has provided many lines of defense within the body, that prevent such a catastrophe.

We have said that putrefactive, poisonous bacteria are easily paralyzed, and put out of commission by acids. If the residues in the bowel can be kept acid, no poisons can be generated, because the toxic bacteria present in nearly all food, will remain out of commission till they are expelled.

How the Colon Fights Toxic Bacteria — In order to accomplish this, the lower bowel of every infant, at birth, is provided with an army of acid-producing bacteria. If the child were permitted to live under perfectly natural conditions, these microscopic plants, known as B. acidophilus, would continue dominant in the colon throughout life, with the result that the blood-stream would not be polluted with poisons from the intestines; sickness would be avoided and youthfulness, vitality and the span of life would be immensely prolonged.

B. Acidophilus Unlike White Blood Corpuscles — The inconceivably minute acidophilus soldiers that Nature employs to protect the colon are often compared with the white corpuscles that defend the blood-stream. But these two kinds of little native body-guards are entirely dissimilar and do their fighting by very different methods. The white blood-corpuscles get rid of bacteria by eating them up, as cats destroy mice. The B. acidophilus, indigenous to the bowel, merely generate a mild acid, harmless to themselves, but fatal or extremely injurious to all putrefactive, poisonous types of bacteria. The acid reaction also stimulates the natural, peristaltic undulations of the bowel and thus brings about regular evacuations.

Unfortunately the conventions of civilization make it impossible to defecate promptly whenever the impulse is felt, with the result that the putrefactive, poisonous bacteria multiply and sooner or later the natural protective little soldiers are completely annihilated.

This total loss of the native acidophilus army frequently happens before people have attained their twenty-fifth birthday, with the result that for the remainder of life the lower bowel becomes a cesspool polluted by billions of alien, injurious microbes.

Some people will say; "Well, if the protective acid-loving soldiers are a part of our inherent physical equipment, how can we continue to live when they have been lost?"

The answer is, that it is possible to survive for

years after many important constituent parts of the body have been extirpated. If this were not so there would be fewer surgical operations. People manage to exist after tonsils, gall-bladder, appendix, prostate-gland, stomach and other useful parts of the body have been removed. But he who retains all the equipment bestowed by Mother Nature has a great advantage over the man who has been mutilated. One may survive the excision of the prostate-gland, or the loss of the native acidophilus, but in either case, the body has been sadly crippled and handicapped.

Unfortunately, ten, fifteen or more years may elapse after the acidophilus army has been driven out before the slightest inconvenience from the loss is experienced. This freedom from suffering is due to the fact that the body is protected in many other ways against poisons produced by the bad bacteria, that always dominate the colon after the friendly flora are gone.

THE LINING OF THE COLON PROTECTS US — The next wall of defense against toxins generated by colon germs is the mucus-membrane of the bowel. Just as the external skin is a perfect suit of armour that will not allow microbes, or their virus to penetrate into the blood, so the colon is provided with a lining that will not permit poisons to pass through.

But as years roll on, the indol, skatol, phenol and other toxins generated by the enemy germs, irritate, inflame and injure this protective mucus-membrane to such an extent, that poisons from the decaying fecal matter, begin to leak through into the blood. But even then the unfortunate victim does not experience the slightest inconvenience and has no inkling that anything is wrong. For the body has more lines of defense that must be passed before any vital organ is attacked.

CHAPTER V

THE LIVER, THE NEXT LINE OF DEFENSE

The next great barrier or fortification against poisons from the bowel entering the general circulation is the liver. This organ is a marvellous laboratory manned by millions of little cells that could teach our most learned chemists many secrets about their profession. Every drop of deleterious matter that leaks into the blood from the bowel is at once destroyed. Indol, for example, a dangerous poison made by putrefactive bacteria in the intestine, is detoxicated in the liver by being mixed, or as we say "conjugated" with etherial sulphates. This transforms the deadly indol into indican, which is entirely harmless.

The toxins from the lower intestine, after being destroyed or made harmless by the little hepatic chemists, are filtered from the blood by the kidneys and expelled in the urine.

In many cases when fecal analysis shows much putrefaction and heavy indol in the colon, the urine, upon examination is found free from indican. This means that little or no damage has yet been sustained by the lining of the bowel and that this line of defense is still intact, and in consequence there is no leakage of toxins into the blood.

TOXINS CAUSE NO DISTRESS SO LONG AS LIVER WORKS WELL — Unfortunately just so long as the liver continues to neutralize toxins received from the bowel, no inconvenience is felt by the victim, and he has not the slightest suspicion of the irreparable damage that continually is going on.

But gradually, one by one, the faithful little chemist-cells of the liver are poisoned, killed and carried off by the blood before they can leave successors to carry on their work. At twenty-one it is estimated a man has thirty million reserve hepatic cells. At forty he may not have half that number and finally the staff of little virus-destroying chemists is so reduced in numbers that poisons pass through the liver into the general circulation without being changed and made harmless, and so it comes to pass that the kidneys are gradually destroyed by contact with the deleterious products generated by putrefactive germs in the colon.

Eventually the polluted blood-stream deteriorates every organ, gland and tissue, thus bringing about those senile changes that are falsely attributed to old age. Degeneration and death are the result of toxins.

It seems unlikely that humanity will ever be able to escape entirely from the damaging effects of the poisonous wastes thrown out by our own tissues — I mean by the billions of microscopic "animals" of which our flesh is made — and therefore, no matter how prolonged our existence on Earth may be, unlike Tennyson's brook, we cannot hope to "go on forever."

But though we cannot avoid the poisons generated by the cells of which our flesh is composed; yet on the other hand, the invasion and domination of the bowels by toxic bacteria, which gradually destroy the body, and cause nearly all human maladies, is unnatural and unnecessary, and can be prevented quite easily if we give Nature a chance.

When this is done, and when we learn to make our eating and other habits, conform to the laws of health, life and youth on this planet will be extended for a much longer period than now obtains — probably for one hundred and fifty years or more.

PSEUDO-ACIDOPHILUS — Whenever science makes discoveries about the conquest of sickness, or the preservation of health, commercial interests invariably rush forward to exploit the new knowledge, for profit. This accounts for the fact that, at the present time, all sorts of devices are being sold to "change the flora." The most popular of these are various cultures of lactic acid bacteria, labelled "acidophilus."

Now the name, acidophilus, is from the Greek and means "acid-loving." It is a generic term and includes several species of bacteria.

The microbes, for example, that multiply in milk, causing it to become sour, are often correctly called "acidophilus." Under the microscope these acid, milk-borne bacteria so closely resemble the protective flora with which Nature endows the bowels at birth, that the most experienced microbiologist finds it almost impossible to tell one species from the other. Yet ordinary acid-loving bacteria are not genuine, protective acidophilus, as truly as brass is not gold, though it glitters.

And there is one infallible test — the kind that are native to the colon will not flourish or survive long outside of the body, while on the other hand B. bulgaricus and other varieties of milk-souring germs, will not live and propagate in the bowels.

Yet these spurious acidophilus bacteria are continually offered for sale with the assurance that they can be successfully implanted in the intestines. Unfortunately, as we have just said, the ordinary lactic acid bacilli soon die when caged in the colon; and, per contra, the genuine intestinal acidophilus are so delicate that they cannot be induced to live and multiply outside of the bowels except in certain media, under the constant care of an experienced microbiologist. And in the earlier stages of their development, a particular uniform warmth must be maintained. For this purpose ingeniously constructed incubators are employed that automatically conserve the correct temperature, no matter what the weather may be.

Genuine acidophilus colon-cultures are therefore extremely scarce and very expensive. Even physicians are sometimes imposed upon with spurious varieties for, of course, few doctors are professional microbiologists.

But frequent experiments prove that even if milk be cultured with genuine acidophilus it will not re-implant the colon when taken by the mouth, because the flora are all digested and killed before they reach the lower bowel.

Of course, any kind of sour milk has one great advantage — it is necessarily free from putrefactive germs, because, as we have said, these bad bacteria cannot multiply in an acid medium.

FLORA FOOD — At the present time, various sugars such as lactose and dextrine are being sold with the statement that they will change the intestinal flora.

Now it is perfectly true that Coli Communis and other varieties of enemy bacteria, that infest the bowel, can, to some extent, be reformed and rendered less virulent, if fed with carbohydrates instead of proteins, but no diet will transform them into genuine acidophilus, any more than a tiger can be turned into a lamb by feeding the brute with vegetables.

If any of the native, protective little soldiers still inhabit the bowel, saccharides like lactose and dextrine, or still better the preparation known as Florafood will enable the friendly microbes to multiply, if any of the species still remain in the bowel. But after these friendly anti-putrefactive bacteria are dead and gone, there is no food that will bring them back to life.

Government regulations of several European countries now make periodic bacteriological examinations of the colon compulsory in the armies, invariably with very great benefit.

In a recent sojourn in France, England and other lands for the purpose of studying modern methods in up-to-date Sanitariums, the author found leading European physicians placing more emphasis upon the necessity of preserving a normal acidophilus flora in the colon as an indispensible factor in the maintenance of perfect health than upon any other condition.

Sir Arbuthnot Lane, President of the New Health Society of England, and the most eminent authority on the gastro-intestinal tract in Europe, in his book, *Secrets of Good Health,* says:

"Certain parts of the intestines teem with low forms of vegetable life, known as bacteria or germs. These plants are of many varieties. If waste products could be removed and fresh glucose broth supplied without limit, a single coccus could in three days' time give rise to progeny weighing a billion times a billion tons.

"It is of the greatest moment that our food supply should be kept safe from the ravages of such greedy pests during the processes of digestion and assimilation. The human digestive tract is of considerable length. The lower few feet constitute the colon or big bowel.

"This part is positively alive with bacteria, but provided that all the nutritive parts of the food have been absorbed into the system by the sterile upper bowel, these bacteria have no opportunity of doing harm. They have to subsist on vegetable fibre and similar remnants from which they cannot manufacture any very poisonous substances.

"The real trouble arises when conditions are so altered that the germs come into contact with rich food. If we choose foods so prepared that twice the normal length of time is required for their liquefaction and absorbtion, some of the food is sure to travel downwards as far as the germ-laden colon before the body can get it out of the way into the tissues. Food and bacteria then meet and putrefaction occurs."

"Bacteria nourished in this way with food meant for our own exclusive use do an immense amount of harm. They decompose the food, making poisons and gas, the effect of which is very much like that of eating stale, putrescent food.

"DEADLIER THAN STRYCHINE — Many of them also produce poisons which they throw off into the surrounding tissues. These complex synthetic bodies are usually called toxins. They are far more lethal than the better-known non-bacterial or chemical poisons, such as arsenic and strychnine. The blood stream spreads their toxins to every part, setting up troubles of the most devastating kinds."

(Page 25, *Secrets of Good Health*, by Sir Arbuthnot Lane.)

But there is one cause for thanksgiving. No matter how long putrefactive types of bacteria may have been dominant in the colon it is always possible to change the flora and to regain the natural protective bacilli if proper measures be taken.

Some time ago, a man came to the author and said he wanted to learn what to eat so as to put on a little more weight. His wife, who was with him, added: "And I would be grateful if my husband could have a special analysis of the feces such as you describe in one of your books that I found in the Public Library."

"Certainly," I replied. "We make many bacteriological examinations of the stool in the Los Angeles laboratory where I am doing research work, and any who join the California Health Education Society that we are organizing, will be given such an analysis, if they so wish."

The man protested that all he needed was a few points on diet, and that to spend four or five dollars on laboratory analysis, would be money thrown away, as he knew there was nothing the matter, because he felt no pain.

"That is no proof there is no malady," I replied. "Even a cancer of the gastro-intestinal tract causes no distress in the initial stage, and often the first indication of the presence of an internal, malignant tumor is disclosed by fecal tests." So he consented.

The analysis showed the stool contained numerous tapeworm's eggs, which of course are invisible, except to a trained eye, with a powerful microscope.

The man took his report to a physician who specializes in such parasites, and a few days later, passed a tapeworm over twenty feet in length.

After this dramatic deliverance the grateful man said: "In the past I have had no use for doctors, believing that health could always be brought about by correct diet, but now I realize that food alone would not have made me perfectly well."

Fortunately the majority are not afflicted with tapeworms, but most people, as a result of unnatural habits, induced by civilized life, are cursed with intestinal conditions that are just as injurious and far more insidious.

The lower bowel of the average person is continually dominated with billions of putrefactive microbes that are constantly generating poisons.

Such individuals may take the food Nature requires, but before a correct diet can be of real benefit, the intestinal flora must be changed.

Chapter VI
FACTORS THAT CAUSE "OLD AGE"

Of the many insect pests of the tropics, none are so destructive as the white ants that work so insidiously destroying timber that their presence is never suspected till a structure tumbles in ruin.

A house may seem to be in perfect repair when a man leaves home in the morning, but when he returns at night, he may find his dwelling a wreck.

But this work of destruction is really not sudden at all. Month after month, millions of ants, concealed in the wood, have been silently gnawing away till nothing is left but a shell that collapses and goes down under the first storm of rain.

Here in this country, homes of another sort are wrecked every year, by still more terrible pests, that work so secretly their presence is never suspected. The dwellings to which we refer are of more value than those made of wood and stone, for they are built of flesh to serve as the home of man's soul. Once they are destroyed, these "houses not made with hands" cannot be restored.

Dwellers in the tropics are continually on the lookout to discover any indcations that may lead them to suspect their homes are being attacked by insects. But few people, no matter in what land they live, ever dream that their bodies are possibly being undermined by innumerable enemies incomparably more destructive than the tropical ants.

How often we see a man in apparent good health suddenly carried off with heart-disease or some other illness. In reality such disaster is not sudden at all. In most cases, the body has been subjected for years to ravages of billions of enemy microbes that are the more terrible because unseen and unsuspected. Of all deadly germs, none takes a heavier toll than the common putrefactive bacteria which are generally present to some extent in the human intestines, but which are usually thought of as not being dangerous to life.

People in tropical lands tell us they have no way of knowing whether their homes are infested with white ants or not. But no man today need be in doubt as to whether his body is harboring enemy microbes.

Analysis by modern methods of a small particle of the feces (i.e., the excreta or waste matter from the bowels), discloses the per cent of every species of germ with as much certainty and precision as a farmer enumerates his live stock. The process is long and intricate, and demands much time, skill and care. The French Government has established free fecal laboratories for the welfare of the people, and a movement is now on foot there to compel every person to submit a specimen of their excreta for analysis at least once a year.

A leading physician of France lately said: "The day is coming when we shall no longer be fooled by our feelings into a false security, but each will have *inside* information about the dangers that menace his health, and will thus avoid disease and premature old age. In the future not *comment vous portez vous*, but, *Quel numero portez vous* will be the way we shall greet our friends." (Not "How are you," but "What is your number," that is: what is your percentage of acidophilus protectors.)

Lately, in England, The National Church has established laboratories for the people for fecal and other analysis by the newer methods.

Some years ago, when the Health Education Society began its work in New York, a canvas was made of existing pathological laboratories to find how many were specializing in fecal analysis by the newer methods. We failed to find one.

In no instance could we discover any analysis that went beyond a more or less painstaking search for parasites, ova or occult blood. Fecal bacteria (of which the average person excretes no less than thirty-three trillion a day, of one kind or another) are ignored as if they were of no importance. Yet a few of these germs, taken at random from any feces and injected into the veins of a guinea-pig, often causes death.

Bacteriological fecal analyses are, of course, made by such establishments as the Rockefeller Institute and by the private laboratories of a few physicians who specialize in intestinal toxemia, but nothing of the kind could we find in the usual pathological laboratories.

There are two reasons for this condition of affairs.

First, the general public, (and even many physicians who are not bacteriologists) know little about the advance that science has made in this direction.

Secondly, a bacteriological analysis of the feces requires a long and elaborate process, and it is difficult to find technicians who have been trained in this special work.

MODERN SCIENCE EXTIRPATES THE TOXIC GERMS BY SIMPLE AND NATURAL MEANS—Now let us go back to our illustration of the white ants. It is difficult for those who live in the tropics to discover whether or not their homes are being undermined by these insect marauders, and it is a still harder task to get rid of the pests, even when they are discovered.

For many years, all attempts to extirpate the toxic bacteria from the intestinal tract were all quite unavailing. The earlier efforts were along the line of driving the poisonous invaders from the bowels by means of germicides and disinfectants, swallowed as medicines by the mouth. But unfortunately, there is no known chemical or drug that will destroy the bad bacteria without injuring the patient at the same time.

The intestinal tract is like a garden, in that it insists on producing some kind of vegetation. Any garden, if not compelled to grow wholesome fruit, flowers or vegetables, will soon be found a mass of noxious weeds. It is so with the human colon.

Bacteria are one-celled plants. In infancy, Nature sows the baby's intestines with such a fine crop of good flora there is no room for poisonous weeds, which too often monopolize man's intestinal tract in later life. A garden must grow something. Cultivate the good flora, and the bad will have no chance to thrive. In the long run, you will find intestinal gardening pays.

However, a warning should again be issued against the many so-called acidophilus cultures in tablets and various preparations to be taken by the mouth. The air is full of pseudo-acidophilus, the kind that causes milk to turn sour, but these little plants will not live in the colon. They are not the species native to the human intestines and will not colonize there.

CHAPTER VII

RE-IMPLANTING THE BOWELS

After the lower bowel has lost its natural germicidal plants and has become a garden of unicelled poisonous weeds, is it possible to have the flora changed? Can we get rid of the bad bacteria and have the native, protective Bacillus Acidophilus completely and permanently restored?

In reply, we are happy to say this can be accomplished, generally without much trouble or expense, and invariably with beneficial results.

Now, the best way of maintaining a farm free from weeds, is to keep the land busy bearing desirable vegetation. The scientific farmer knows that in order to grow good crops, the soil must have a generous supply of the special elemental bricks required in the construction of carrots, cabbages, corn, or whatever he wishes to harvest.

This task would be more simple if there were some magic way of changing the composition of the soil. Then a farmer might starve unfriendly flora, like twitch and thistles, by robbing the land of elements required by these weeds, and at the same time he could accelerate the growth of his crops, by adding minerals and other constituents essential to the vegetation he wished to produce.

In intestinal gardening something very like this can be done. For the old proverb, "What is one man's meat, is another man's poison," is literally true when applied to bacteria. The food on which friendly flora flourish, starves putrefactive germs.

But before entering upon the question of how to change the soil of our intestinal garden so as to aid in bringing about the desired results, it may be advisable to say something about the habits of civilization that cripple the colon, cursing us with constipation which causes most of the ills of humanity.

X-Ray examinations show that food passes through the stomach and small intestines, a distance of twenty-five feet, in eight hours or less, that is, an average of four hours in the stomach and the same length of time in the small intestine. Nothing of benefit to the system is left in the refuse when it reaches the lower bowel, and therefore this excreta should be expelled from the body as soon as possible.

As the colon is only five feet in length and nothing remains to be done to the refuse when it reaches this section except to dismiss it from the body, if the speed at which the food has been moving were maintained, the residues would accomplish the balance of the journey to the exit in less than two hours. This would be long before the time limit of the bad bacteria's slumber expired, and consequently these evil germs would be safely out of the body ere they awoke and began their nefarious business.

Wild creatures get rid of the wastes of digestion many times daily, at least once after every meal.

Even domestic animals like horses and cows average a bowel movement every two hours. Household pets, such as dogs, are generally "house-broken," that is, they have been trained to refrain from defecation until such times as they are permitted to go out of doors. The result is, that these poor creatures are generally extremely constipated.

Wild, native races in all parts of the world, defecate four or five times daily, whenever and wherever the impulse is felt. In this respect at least, civilization, with its conventions and restraints, is far from being an unmixed blessing.

When mankind awakens to the tremendous importance of expelling excreta at regular and frequent intervals, public toilets will be provided at every street corner and in the center of each block.

Infants, like savages, begin life by having four or five movements of the bowel daily. But when they arrive at the run-about age, they are carefully trained by mothers and nurses to resist the calls of nature. At school, at play, at church and everywhere, they are educated to restrain the impulse to defecate, no matter how imperative; and in course of time, the bowel gets accustomed to having but one movement in twenty-four hours.

As a result of these delays, fecal matter is frequently retained for days. The colon, in consequence of the increased weight, is often sagged out of place, which still further retards and delays the passage of decaying refuse.

Many people declare that they are not constipated because they have a motion every night or each morning, as the case may be. But the important point is not merely the regularity, or even the frequency of defecation, but the length of time the food residues have been on their journey.

Light from some constellations takes millions of years to reach this earth, but the rays from these orbs come to us as regularly, and as frequently, as the luminous vibrations of the sun, which make their trip in eight minutes. The bowel movements of many are as regular as the rays from Sirius or Betelguese, but the transit like the light from these remote stars, takes too long. When food residues are delayed in the colon, putrefaction inevitably takes place.

The best way of finding out a person's motility period—that is, the length of time it takes the food to pass through the body—is to swallow a charcoal or carmine capsule when taking a meal. Bowel movements are then carefully watched until the color appears in the feces. On trying this simple, harmless test, many "regular" people are astonished to find their dinner does not show up for several days; in some cases, a week may elapse before a trace of the marker appears in the stool.

But many people are the victims of auto-intoxication who do not seem to be constipated. Indeed, some of the worst cases of injury from chronic bowel poisoning occurs in those who habitually have several evacuations each day.

In what way then can a person discover whether or not they are afflicted with intestinal toxemia?

In reply we would say the only method of finding out whether enemy bacteria are flooding the body with poison is by a bacteriological analysis of the feces. Unfortunately, in many cities this cannot be obtained. Few doctors are bacteriologists, for microbiology is a separate profession and includes such a vast field, that a life-time is too short to cover the whole subject.

Some time ago when I questioned a gardener about the mineral content of a new kind of potato, he said, "I know nothing about potatoes, my specialty is roses."

Microscopic plant life is wider and more varied than the flora with which the farmer or gardener has to deal, and the bacteriologist who tries to become thoroughly familiar with the habits of all the weeds and flowers that thrive in that most prolific of all gardens, the lower bowel, must devote years of special study to this subject.

The fecal analysis given by most clinical laboratories confines itself to chemical and microscopic tests for undigested starch granules, occult blood, animal parasites, ova, etc. Bacteria are ignored as of no importance. Yet, if a few drops of the toxins, manufactured by putrefactive germs from the so-called, normal bowel, are injected into the veins of a small animal, such as a rabbit or guinea-pig, the creature generally develops blood poisoning and dies.

There are several reasons why few laboratories include cultural tests in their fecal examinations. First, this special work requires much time. Incubation cannot be hurried.

Secondly, not many laboratories and still fewer technicians, are fully equipped for this particular specialty, and, thirdly, as we said before, few doctors are microbiologists.

Nevertheless, in many large cities there is now at least one laboratory that really makes bacteriological tests in their analysis of the stool, and generally some doctors can be found who have specialized in this work.

If the fecal report shows, that, in spite of the presence of putrefactive bacteria, there is a remnant of the genuine acidophilus Bacillus still left, every effort should be made at once to encourage the growth of these precious protective flora.

Now the natural foods for these good little plants are carbohydrates, especially lactose and dextrine. There are many preparations of these simple sugars on the market, but in our experience, by far the best for the purpose, is a mixture known as

Florafood, put out by the Health Education Society. Doctors generally prescribe two tablespoonfuls of Florafood in a glass of warm water, half an hour before each meal. The object being to flood the stomach with more of this carbohydrate than can be assimilated by the system, so that the undigested surplus may overflow into the lower bowel and feed the friendly bacteria in the colon. But the sugar tolerance of most people is extremely limited and the excess necessitated by this method is very trying to the pancreas, and sometimes brings about a nervous, upset condition of the whole body.

Instead of administering by the mouth, a far better plan is to mix a teaspoonful of the powder in half a glass of warm water and inject the solution directly into the rectum, employing for this purpose a small rectal syringe such as is used for babies. A suitable apparatus known as an infant rectal syringe, can be bought at any drug store for about twenty-five cents.

If the administration of Florafood does not result in such an increase of acidophilus that the putrefactive bacteria are entirely expelled in the course of a few weeks, genuine cultures of Bacillus Acidophilus should be injected into the rectum. For this purpose a very concentrated, non-protein culture, containing not less than three billion viable plants per cubic centimeter, should be used. Unfortunately, *genuine* acidophilus is very expensive and exceedingly hard to obtain.

So-called acidophilus milk, as explained elsewhere in this book, is quite useless for this purpose.

Most makes of lactose and dextrine bear on the box a legend to the effect that the mixture will "change the flora." This statement is cruelly misleading. It is undoubtedly true that bad germs fed on such food will, to some extent, experience a change of heart and generate less virulent poisons, but putrefactive germs cannot be converted into acidophilus, no matter what diet you give them.

Every gardener knows that a generous supply of proper fertilizer will result in good crops when there are any roots, seeds or plants to be nourished; but all the fertilizer in the world will not produce one blade of grass, on a plot that is devoid of any form of vegetable life.

When analysis proves Bacillus acidophilus to be entirely absent from the colon, fresh cultures should be reimplanted. When this has been accomplished, the natural aciduric bacteria will remain permanently dominant in the lower bowel, if a proper diet be followed.

It is most important to keep in mind the fact that the most fearful toxic condition may exist for years in the lower bowel, but so long as the liver and other anti-toxic organs are able to destroy the poisons, the patient may not feel any inconvenience, and will have no suspicion that his constitution is being gradually undermined.

It is generally useless for a physician to explain to such persons that their fecal analysis reveals the presence of enemy bacteria. They merely remark that they are feeling fine, and are confident that their own sensations are a better indication of their condition than any scientific diagnosis. But sooner or later the day comes when the defensive organs can no longer cope with the situation, because, through long over-work, these delicate machines begin to wear out. As a result, harmful products circulate through the whole body and whatever part happens to be weakest, is the first to suffer.

In some the heart is impaired as the result of this auto-intoxication. In others the stomach becomes deranged and indigestion, with its attendant evils—gas, and eventually perhaps ulcers—cause fearful distress.

Many other maladies may owe their origin to intestinal toxemia, such as nervousness, insomnia, high blood-pressure and catarrh in all forms. What are commonly called colds are mostly due to this cause, also rheumatism, headaches and other ills too numerous to mention.

The question is often asked, "Will changing the flora cure the maladies the bad bacteria have caused?"

In reply we would say, that removing the putrefactive germs and replacing these enemies with the natural flora will stop further mischief, but this happy exchange will not at once repair the ravages the little devils have done. If your house has been closed all the summer and you return to find that rats from the cellar have ruined the upholstery, the piano, and other furniture, you naturally send for the rat-catcher to rid your house of vermin. But destroying the rats and replacing them with a strong guard of cats will not repair your piano. It will merely prevent further mischief.

Or, to change the illustration. In the good old days when the fair sex enhanced their loveliness with large floral headgear, the author, on one occasion, offered his umbrella to a lady whose hat—a garden of artificial flowers—was in danger of being ruined by a sudden shower. But his silken shield was powerless to restore such flowers as had already been ruined by the storm. It merely saved from further injury those parts that had not been destroyed. In the same way, removing bad bacteria will not of itself repair such organs of the body as have already been poisoned and degenerated.

But if the flowers, instead of being artificial had been living plants in a real garden, in process of time, Nature might have restored them.

So the organs of the body are not artificial and dead. If protected from further injury, Nature, in process of time, generally rebuilds stomach, kidneys, heart, lungs and all other parts to a healthy condition. But all such natural processes are slowly accomplished, and they are brought about, not by medicines and doctors, but by the restorative powers of Nature.

CHAPTER VIII

HOW THE AUTHOR'S YOUTH
WAS RENEWED

One morning, many years ago, as I stood in the office of a great specialist undergoing a physical examination, the physician turned to me and said: "You are a pretty old man."

"What age do you take me to be?" I asked.

"Upwards of seventy," he replied.

Thinking the man was joking, I laughed and said: "Everyone gives me credit for being a patriarch. Why, I was born in ____."

"I don't care when you were born," he interrupted. "You are an old man. Senility is not a question of the calendar—not a mere matter of the number of years since we came into the world. The degenerated condition of the body called 'old age' is merely a register of the damage that has been done to our organs and tissues by various poisons. You have the worst case of intestinal toxemia I have seen in a man of your years. Your urinalysis shows a three plus of indican, and the fecal examination proves that the bowels are filled with putrefactive types of bacteria and the toxins generated by these germs have poisoned and degenerated every tissue and organ of your body."

"But the flora can easily be changed, Doctor," I protested. For in the days when I was majoring in science, before studying as a medical missionary, I had gone in for microbiology and felt I knew a good deal about the subject.

"That may be," he returned, "but the damage has already been done. Changing the flora in your case, would be like locking the stable door after the horse has been stolen. Every tissue of your body is badly degenerated and damaged."

Other great specialists confirmed this diagnosis. For a man in middle life to learn that his kidneys, heart and other vital organs are worn out, and that there is nothing between him and the grave, but a year or so of suffering, is discouraging. But I determined not to give up without a struggle. Most Englishmen fight best when nearly beaten.

Metschnikoff, of the Pasteur Institute, had just startled the scientific world by his discovery of the protective flora of the colon. Sick as I was, I decided to go to Paris and learn what could be done in my case.

At the end of a year I returned to England much improved. The ugly, brown patches, diagnosed by skin specialists as "senile keratosis" had disappeared from my forehead, my blood pressure was lower, and the continual intestinal distress, that had tortured me night and day for years, had entirely gone; though my pulse was still frightfully irregular, and other conditions of the body were far from normal.

Nevertheless my friends were astonished at the

improvement in my appearance. Some physicians smiled at the "bug" explanation and attributed my bettered condition to various causes. But microscopic and other tests showed that the toxic bacteria of the colon had been replaced by the anti-putrefactive variety, and I felt sure that the alteration in my physical condition was due to the change of flora.

IMPLANTED SELF WITH B. ACIDOPHILUS — During my stay in Paris, I had become familiar with newer methods of fecal examination and of germ culture. Knowing the terrible fight my body-guard of friendly bacteria were having to maintain their ground against billions of putrefactive enemies that daily gain entrance through food, I spent much of my time in raising regiments of protective soldiers, and thus my army of the interior received fresh recruits every day.

My desire to learn more of the effects that intestinal germs play in the health and diseases of the body, led me to make arrangements with London laboratories and hospitals, by means of which I received many fecal specimens for study, together with the history of the patients in each case.

The data thus compiled proved to myself and to the bacteriologists associated with me, that Metschnikoff's theory is true; though his sour-milk plan for changing flora, effective in the test tube, fails in the intestines, first, because B. bulgaricus, and other lactic acid bacilli he employed, are not in their natural habitat in the colon and cannot keep alive there, and, secondly, because cultures, taken by the mouth, are digested and destroyed in the stomach and small intestines, and seldom reach the lower bowel in viable form.

During the time that I was engaged in these special bacteriological studies, I was a student of chemistry and microbiology in London. For directly I returned from Paris, I determined to go back to school, to learn as much as possible about food and the science of nutrition; because I was sure that my intestinal toxemia and the many maladies that followed in the wake of my auto-intoxication had their origin in years of incorrect eating habits.

But the things I learned in class and from books about diet, were not nearly so valuable as what I found out for myself by experiments on my own body.

Bio-chemists, today, make most of their discoveries about food, by experiments on guinea-pigs, rats, rabbits and other animals. I had no menagerie of this kind. I was my own guinea pig.

For years I kept a record of all that I ate at every meal. And each day, and sometimes every few hours, I gave myself a complete urinalysis, and a thorough bacteriological examination of the stool, also blood and other tests. In this way, by the effects they had on my body, I gradually learned what foods were good for me, and what to avoid.

One of my first discoveries was that citric acid fruits, like oranges and lemons, had an alkaline reaction. My fundamental trouble had been acidosis. My urine often showed a fearful excess of acidity.

One day I lunched on nothing but oranges. The weather was very hot, and I think I must have taken a dozen. I was just convalescing, after six weeks in bed with inflamatory rheumatism — my third attack of that excruciating malady. I knew that oranges were contra-indicated in my case, or, at any rate, in those days, all the authorities said they increased the acidity. So after indulging in my orange orgie, I expected to find an alarming increase of acid in the urine.

But to my amazement, when I titrated the kidney-secretion with phenolphthalein and sodium hydroxide, I found that the urine had suddenly become alkaline. When I told this experience to professional dietetians they laughed and said I was crazy. But I repeated the experiment on myself, and on others, many times, and always with the same result. Therefore, since that day—more than twenty years ago— I have taken for lunch, nothing but oranges or grape fruit, and have never been troubled with rheumatism or acidity since.

In the same way, I found out what foods were best to maintain a normal flora in the colon, what foods produced the most erythrocytes and hemoglobin, and kept the blood-pressure normal: what was best to eat so as to avoid indigestion, gas, headache, indicanuria, and many other troubles.

During the time that I was occupied in changing the flora, I abstained from all meat, living entirely on vegetable foods, even eliminating dairy products. My protein intake at this time was about sixty grams daily, mostly in the form of finely pulverized English walnuts.

As my health steadily improved under this regime, I planned to continue my vegetarian diet with the addition of a glass of fresh, unpasteurized milk at breakfast.

But it disturbed me that Liebig, Rubner, Voit, Atwater and others, who at that time were held indisputable authorities on alimentation, insisted that a vegetarian diet, though adequate to sustain life, was inadvisable, because, they contended, the highest physical well-being could not be maintained, long, without the addition of flesh foods. (See Chap. "What About Meat?", unabridged edition of this book.)

Vegetable protein is often incomplete, that is to say, it frequently does not contain all the seventeen amino-acids, and, therefore, the bio-chemists insisted that it was ncessary for human beings to supplement products of the soil with nitrogenous food of animal origin. Moreover, the nutrition experts said, that, inasmuch as the protein of plants is not so readily digested and assimilated as meat, it was simply slow suicide for me to confine myself to a diet exclusively composed of soil-grown products.

Persuaded by these arguments, I added a little flesh food to my bill of fare. This consisted generally of a small piece of chicken or a chop, two or three times a week.

But after even this slight indulgence, in my then degenerated condition, I always noticed putrefactive types of bacteria in my fecal analysis, and I returned to a strictly vegetarian diet until I had again gotten rid of the B. coli, B. welchi and other varieties of poisonous germs.

Theoretically, from reading of standard authorities, I was convinced that in order to keep well, permanently, I must eat meat, but each time that I returned to a carnivorous manner of living, toxic bacteria reappeared in the stool and indican became quite heavy in the urine.

Thus, for about two years, I oscillated backwards and forwards, between vegetarianism and a mixed diet. At last, convinced by scientific tests that my physical condition was better when I took fruits and vegetables, I resolved to confine myself to soil-grown products, supplemented by a little raw milk and cottage cheese, and occasionally the yolks (but not the whites) of two eggs. By the aid of urine, fecal, blood and other analysis, I have tested out diets on hundreds of people of all ages, in all walks of life, and have invariably obtained best results from a lacto-ovo-vegetarian diet.

What a change has taken place in the minds of physiologists in the last twenty years. When I began my experiments, practically all the professional biochemists insisted that at least one hundred twenty grams of protein, per day, were essential to keep the average person in nitrogenous equilibrium. Today, as a result of the epoch making experiments of Chittendon, Hindhede and others, the nutrition experts of the world are pretty well agreed that sixty grams of protein, per day, is ample for the average person, and that an excess of nitrogenous food, especially when drawn from the animal kingdom, is the cause of most of the ill-health of the civilized world. Mc-Collum, Hopkins and other authorities are agreed that a lacto-ovo-vegetarian diet is the ideal for vigorous health.

When more fuel foods (carbohydrates and hydro-carbons) than the body can use, are taken, the surplus is packed away in the tissues for future use, in the form of fat. But when a higher percentage of building material, (protein) than is required for growth or repair is eaten, the excess cannot be stored in the body, so a great deal of needless toil is thrown upon the kidneys and other organs of excretion to get rid of the redundant nitrogen, and this extra, entirely unnecessary, work wears out these delicate, complicated machines.

When the diet contains more than eight per cent of nitrogenous food (meat, eggs, cheese, nuts) the urea in the urine mounts rapidly, but the blood, fortunately, maintains the same proportion of protein. This is due to the vigilant activity of the kidneys; but this strenuous, forced labor, permanently injures these vital organs. Moreover, some of the superfluous, building food finds its way into the lower bowel and provides a feast for the putrefactive, poison-producing germs.

Of course young people need a higher relative ratio of nitrogenous food than adults, because they must have material for growth as well as repair. Human beings develop faster during the first nine months of their existence, than at any other time, and consequently, their food should have a larger proportion of building stuff then, than later, when growth is slower, or has stopped.

Now mother's milk averages only 1.7 per cent of protein. This gives the infant less than one calorie a day per pound, which is less than one-third of the amount, per pound, eaten by adults. If this proportion of nitrogenous material suffices for that period of life when growth is most rapid, it is certainly enough for adults when protein is merely required for repair.

Some people have expressed fear that the diets I suggest are too low in protein. But as a matter of fact, my own meals always contain a much higher ratio of complete nitrogenous material than Nature provides for the baby during the first six months, when the child is increasing in size more quickly, than at any other time. And analysis proves this amount of protein is more than sufficient. The secret of success is to give the body all the nitrogenous food it needs, without any excess to injure the liver, kidneys and colon.

Of course, regaining the natural intestinal bacilli does not of itself rebuild the body that has been injured. But if we keep putrefaction from the intestines by maintaining a normal flora, and take proper food, Nature, in due time, will rebuild every gland and tissue, and we shall be so strong and well, that sickness in any form will not trouble us, and we shall seem to grow younger.

This has been the experience of the author of this book, and of others. It may be the good fortune of every one, who takes the trouble to learn to live in harmony with the laws of Nature.

CHAPTER IX
CONQUER CONSTIPATION NATURE'S WAY, BY SWALLOWING A SPONGE EVERY DAY

To move regularly, frequently and naturally, the bowel flora must be dominated by the native B. acidophilus.

Moreover, in order that putrefactive germs traveling through the gastro-intestinal tract in food residues, may not have time to penetrate and multiply in the lower intestines, the bowels must, also, be supplied with enough *bulk, moisture* and *lubrication* to cause several natural evacuations each day. A lack of any one of these three things invariably brings about constipation. Unfortunately, most of the food that passes through the digestive machinery of civilized people is deficient in all of these qualities, and the inevitable result is, that the refuse becomes impacted and decomposed in the lower bowel. That is to say, the ever present spores of bad bacteria in the delayed fecal matter, hatch out, and convert the colon into a seething cesspool of poisons.

The protective aciduric flora stimulates the peristaltic movement of the bowel. But in addition to this, the colon must be provided with three things that Nature demands, namely, bulk, moisture and lubrication. The easiest way to accomplish this, is to swallow a sponge soaked in liquid at every meal. By a sponge we mean some non-digestible, moisture absorbing, variety of woody fibre.

For a long time, the physicians and food-chemists of the Health Education Society, endeavored to find an ideal form of cellulose that would act in the same way as the juice-soaked fibrous foods of prehistoric man. And finally, after years of experimentation a preparation which we called B.M.L. was discovered.

Through the generosity of well-to-do members of the Health Education Society, many thousands of packages of this remarkable sea-vegetable sponge have been given to the poor. All profits from the sale of B.M.L are used to extend the work of this Society. An additional merit of this anti-constipation mixture is that it supplies iodine, iron, and other minerals in an organic form, due to the fact that the marine plants it contains are very rich in these elements.

B.M.L is not a drug, medicine or cathartic. It is an auxiliary, cellulose food, and acts in a natural way by supplying the factors the bowels require.

All cathartics, purgatives and laxatives are injurious. That is the reason the body tries to expel them.

The mucous membrane of the eye, when irritated by any foreign substance, immediately pours out a fluid in order that the offending matter may be washed away. The lining of the intestines acts upon cathartics and laxatives in precisely the same manner. Purgatives are said to "move the bowels."

In reality the bowels move the purgatives, in order to get rid of them. Laxatives do not act upon the body, but the body acts upon them, drawing water from the blood to flush the injurious irritants out of the system.

All purgatives are poisons. Castor oil, epsom salts, jalap, magnesia, senna, cascara, phenolphthalein, rhubarb, podophyllin, aloes, and all the much advertised, harmless, (?) vegetable and herbal laxatives, (which are merly disguised combinations of the above mentioned or similar drugs), are habit-forming and injurious, and that is why Nature gets rid of them as quickly as possible by pushing and washing them out of the bowels.

"But," Mr. E. Z. Mark will object, "Movemquik" is different. Professor Foolem says "Movemquik" is composed of herbs and vegetables and is therefore entirely harmless."

That word "vegetables" gets the gullibles every time. They forget that thousands of the most deadly poisons, such as strychnine, opium, morphine, belladona, cocaine and nicotine are from the vegetable kingdom.

The official method of capital punishment in ancient Greece was not hanging or decapitation but consisted in the compulsory drinking of a cup of hemlock — the juice of a plant. Every school-boy knows that Socrates was executed in that way. What is more deadly than strychnine? Yet this swift and terrible poison is a vegetable. Nevertheless, thousands of people are fooled into thinking that because a laxative is guaranteed to be composed of plants or herbs it must necessarily be entirely harmless. So let the truth be repeated with emphasis. All laxatives of which less than a teaspoon will produce a movement — that is, any kind of a "lax" that does not depend upon moisture-absorbing bulk — is injurious, and the copious bowel movement, following the use of such drug, is due to the system trying to eject the poison with all the speed possible.

When the habit of taking such deleterious medicines has become formed, it is not wise to discontinue the practice too suddenly or there may be a partial or complete blockade of the bowels, if deprived of their usual irritant, and the consequent delay of fecal matter will enable the bad bacteria to generate a vast increase of toxins.

Therefore it is often better to continue for a time to blast out the debilitated intestinal tract with the accustomed, injurious explosives until the natural flora have become dominant and the weakened colon has regained some of its normal strength.

Fortunate indeed is the person who has never begun the pernicious habit of dosing with purgatives or laxatives. For sooner or later they bring about a prolapsed, spastic or other deformed, abnormal condition of the colon.

"Cathartics have shortened the lives of millions," declared Dr. Osler on one occasion. This is undoubtedly so. But, on the other hand, it is also true that the majority of people are constipated and many of them are unaware of that fact. And constipation, with its inevitable multiplication of teeming billions of poison-producing bacteria, is the cause of ninety-eight per cent of all maladies and of premature old age.

In his diet of leaves and buds, shoots and fruits and roots, our prehistoric ancestors naturally consumed much woody fibre (cellulose).

Meals, as served in most homes and restaurants, are too refined and practically devoid of roughage. What little cellulose is left in the food is rendered soft and almost useless for peristaltic purposes by cooking.

Meat, milk, cheese, eggs, white flour, sugar, etc., are almost completely digested and absorbed into the blood, leaving little or no residue to stimulate the muscular movements in the intestines.

It is therefore necessary to take an auxilliary food containing a good variety of moisture-absorbing cellulose.

Bran was formerly frequently prescribed for the purpose of giving bulk to the feces, but bran is far from ideal, because it does not absorb much moisture, and has a tendency to pack and accumulate in the colon ,thus augmenting the evils it is intended to cure.

The mucilaginous cellulose of B.M.L never packs and this is one of the reasons why we believe it is the best natural laxative, science has yet discovered.

In the second place, in order that the bowels may move naturally, the wastes of digestion must be kept very moist. To accomplish this a plentiful supply of liquid must reach the colon.

With this object in view, people are often urged to drink a great deal of water. Now the drinking of a reasonable quantity of water, preferably distilled, is an excellent way to help the kidneys to rid the blood-stream of poisons, but it is an error to think that beverages that enter the mouth pass through the body via the colon. As a matter of fact, most of the water and other liquids are switched from the alimentary canal into the blood-stream soon after they leave the stomach.

Free liquid, that is, liquid that has not been absorbed by food, passes through the walls of the small intestines into the blood tubes and travels along these channels to the kidneys. These organs filter the excess of water from the blood and finally the discarded fluid is discharged as urine.

Owing to the fact that liquids are detoured from the intestinal tract and travel along the blood-stream till they leave the body by way of the kidneys and bladder, the colon generally suffers from lack of moisture, and this is one of the principle causes of constipation.

Rabbits, sheep and many other animals never drink water if they are living in a natural environment, because their diet consists of moisture-soaked cellulose like grass, and this acts as a sponge to carry water to the bowel. Experiments prove that liquids contained in woody fibre do not pass through the villi of the intestinal walls into the blood. Therefore animals on a diet of juicy plants never suffer from constipation and their excrement is always extremely soft.

But dry foods that compel graminivorous creatures, like sheep and rabbits, to drink liquids, always bring about a costive condition of the colon.

Comparative anatomy leads us to believe that primeval man naturally partook of much succulent, vegetable food, and in this way the bowels were always well supplied with bulk and with moisture.

B.M.L is a scientific attempt to provide absorbent, cellulose food, rich in minerals, and in mucilaginous qualities that lubricate the intestines.

For it must be remembered that the third factor essential to natural bowel movement is lubrication.

A few years ago the appendix was thought to be a useless vestigial structure with no present-day function. But it is now known that this little blind pouch is really the oil-can that secretes a mucilagenous fluid for the purpose of lubricating the colon.

Unfortunately the diet and unnatural habits of civilized life injure the appendix so that in many people it has become atrophied and useless.

In such cases, certain foods that naturally lubricate the bowels should be taken, not merely every day, but at each meal. The best substance known to science at the present time, for this purpose, is the remarkable, non-digestible mucilage of certain African seeds. These are included in B.M.L.

Sometimes constipated people drink olive oil for the purpose of lubricating the colon. But fats and oils taken by the mouth never reach the lower bowel. All hydro-carbons such as cream, butter, lard and oils, are chemically united with alkalies in the small intestine, converted into a soluble form and absorbed into the lymph and blood and so never reach the large intestine.

For many years chemistry knew of only one exception to this rule and that was petroleum. Mineral oil is never digested in the intestinal tract and therefore is not absorbed through the villi into the blood, but passes unchanged into the colon, greasing the walls of the lower bowel as it passes through. Therefore, for some years paraffin oil was considered an ideal laxative because it acted in a purely mechanical way. But no doctor who is a specialist on the gastro-intestinal tract prescribes mineral oil today, for the simple reason that there is abundant evidence to prove that all rock-derived hydro-carbons, if habitually taken, are liable to produce cancer. Whenever biologists, for the sake of experiment, wish to bring about malignant tumors in animals, they employ coal-tar products.

Fortunately, just when the scientific world became aware of the dangers of mineral oil, a vegetable lubricant, without any of the disadvantages of paraffin, was discovered.

The name of this plant is Psyllium Plantago and the seeds alone are used. They contain a peculiar kind of mucilaginous substance that is not affected by the digestive juices, and so passes unchanged through the colon, oiling the walls as it goes.

But the name psyllium is a generic term; there are many kinds. All yield a copious supply of oil, but some varieties are ineffective because the mucilaginous substance they give forth is digested and absorbed in the small intestine and so never reaches the colon. Like flax-seed, these digestible kinds of psyllium are nourishing and fattening and therefore useless for bowel lubrication. Much of the psyllium sold today is really the digestible variety and consequently utterly worthless as a lubricant. Yet these cheap substitutes seem to accomplish the same result. But the laxative effect is often due to the presence of some cathartic drug, surreptitiously added to the seed.

The lubricating feature of B.M.L is largely due

to psyllium — the genuine seed that is not digested and absorbed, but passes unchanged into the lower bowel.

I believe I was the first to make known the virtues of psyllium to the civilized world. Years ago, when in Africa, I learned of these marvellous seeds from a Medical Missionary, who had been laboring many years in the heart of the Dark Continent. This Missionary Doctor told me how the natives took these seeds as a bowel lubricant and were never sick from the fevers and malarias that killed white people.

After satisfying myself of the virtues of these unique seeds — the first and only non-digestible, vegetable lubricant known — I carried them to England, and afterwards to America, and my books describing their virtues, written years ago, may be found in most public libraries. These genuine, non-digestible, lubricating seeds were then added to our sea-weed sponge mixture and the name B.M.L was adopted and registered by us in the United States Patent Office.

In the last ten years innumerable attempts, by unscrupulous manufacturers, have been made to imitate B.M.L; but most of these pirated, pseudo mixtures are found on examination to contain the ordinary, cheap, digestible varieties of psyllium and substitute varieties of sea-weeds and often some kind of purgative to make up for the lack of natural lubri-

action. Some have even presumed to forge the name B.M.L.

All profits from the sale of B.M.L are used for the work of the Health Education Society.

It is important to remember that the laxative effect of B.M.L is due to three things. First, *bulk*, which is supplied by the dessicated marine moss.

Second, *moisture*. The sea-weeds, like a sponge, absorb an abundance of water, and the liquid, held fast by the cellulose, cannot escape through the walls of the small intestine into the blood-stream. The water, therefore, is carried through the entire length of the lower bowel, dissolving the dried feces and washing out the walls of the colon.

Third, *lubrication*. The abundance of non-digestible vegetable oil lubricates the whole length of the intestines, thus further facilitating the passage of the feces.

B.M.L, therefore, merely adds to other food the bulk, moisture and lubrication the lower bowel requires to enable it to function naturally. It is not habit-forming, but strengthens the intestinal muscles by exercise.

Thousands of cases of chronic constipation have had their normal function completely restored by persistence with this simple, natural, supplementary food.